PLAY THE PART

POLICE OFFICER

Written by Liz Gogerly

Photographs by Chris Fairclough

WAYLAND

First published in 2011
by Wayland

Copyright © Wayland 2011

Wayland
338 Euston Road
London NW1 3BH

Wayland Australia
Level 17/207 Kent Street
Sydney, NSW 2000

Editor: Paul Humphrey
Design: D. R. ink
Commissioned Photography: Chris Fairclough
Picture credits: West Midlands Police: pp. 4, 5, 6, 12 top.

British Library Cataloguing in Publication Data
Gogerly, Liz.
    Police officer. -- (Play the part)
    1. Police--Juvenile literature. 2. Police--Juvenile
    drama. 3. Role playing--Juvenile literature.
    I. Title II. Series
    363.2'2-dc22

ISBN 978 0 7502 6504 1

Printed in China

Wayland is a division of Hachette Children's Books,
an Hachette UK Company

www.hachette.co.uk

Contents

What is a police officer?   4

Things to make and do
Dress like a police officer   6
The front desk   8
The police station   10
Officers on call!   12

Play the part
The missing ring   14
Help, I'm lost!   16
The bike accident   18
Caught in the act!   20
Caught in the act! (continued)   22

Glossary   24
Index   24

What is a police officer?

A police officer has an important job in the **community**. Part of their job is to stop people breaking the **law**.

A police officer is somebody that we can trust. If you are lost you can ask a police officer for help. If you need **directions** you can always ask a police officer.

The police also deal with all kinds of emergencies. A busy police officer may have to deal with a traffic accident and a **burglary** all in one day!

Dress like a police officer

Most police officers wear a black **uniform** with a white shirt. They often wear a yellow jacket over the top too. You can wear your own clothes or buy an outfit. Shops sell police officer uniforms for dressing up. You can also buy toy helmets, **handcuffs** and **personal radios**.

Make a police badge

Police officers always wear a badge on their uniform. This is how you make your own police officer's badge.

You will need:
* ★ Thin white card
* ★ Thin blue card
* ★ Thin yellow paper
* ★ Kitchen foil
* ★ Pencil
* ★ Glue
* ★ Sticky tape
* ★ Safety pin
* ★ Scissors

(1) Draw a badge shape like this on the piece of white card. You can trace this one.

(2) Ask an adult to help cut out the shape.

3 Spread glue on one side of the badge. Lay the sticky side down onto a piece of kitchen foil.

4 Cut around the badge, leaving a bit extra around the sides. Fold the foil over the edges.

5 Cut out a circle of blue card and a smaller circle of yellow paper.

6 Write 'POLICE' on the yellow paper.

7 Glue the yellow paper onto the blue card and stick them onto the badge.

8 Ask an adult to help use sticky tape to attach a safety pin to the back of the badge.

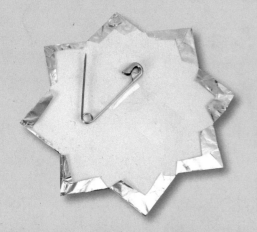

The front desk

Most police stations have a front desk. This is the place where anyone can go for help. A **police neighbourhood support officer** is usually on duty at the front desk. They help people with reporting crimes and lost property. They give **advice** and help people in all kinds of situations.

You will need:

★ A table
★ A telephone
★ A computer
★ Notebooks
★ Pens
★ Posters for the walls

Set up your own front desk

Make the table into a front desk. Arrange the telephone, computer, notebooks and pens on the desk.

You could get some posters from your local police station to decorate the walls (see Halloween poster below). Another idea is to make your own posters. Why not make posters warning drivers to 'Slow Down!' or to 'Watch Out for Thieves'.

In an emergency call 999 and ask for the police.

HALLOWEEN

Sussex Police want your help!

If you are going to go out trick or treating, please do not call on the elderly or anyone else who might be afraid.

We want you to have fun, but in a safe and friendly way.

Thank you

www.sussex.police.uk

Watch OUT

THIEVES ARE OUT!

POLICE

The police station

The police station is a busy place. Police officers work hard **solving** and preventing crimes. Sometimes they take **fingerprints** of **suspects**. Suspects are often interviewed to see what they know.

Taking fingerprints

1. Press the tips of your fingers down hard on the ink stamp.

2. Place your inky fingertips onto a piece of paper. Press hard to make the fingerprints.

3. Add the name of the suspect and the date of when the prints were taken.

You will need:

★ Paper
★ Ink stamp pad

NAME:

DATE :

11

Officers on Call!

Police officers on the **beat** or in their cars stay in touch with the police station using their police radios. If there is an emergency the police station contacts the police officer and tells them what they need to do.

Make your own police radio

1 Paint the box with black paint.

2 Cut out a rectangle of white paper to make the screen for the radio.

3 Write 'POLICE RADIO' and a made-up mobile phone number on the paper.

POLiCE RADiO
015673002X1

You will need:

★ An empty cardboard box about the same size as a mobile phone
★ Paper
★ 1 small felt-tip pen lid
★ 1 large felt-tip pen lid
★ A sheet of white paper
★ 12 plain dot stickers
★ Black paint
★ Colour felt-tip pens
★ Glue
★ Sticky tape

4 Glue the paper to the top of the front of the police radio.

5 Stick the dot stickers underneath the screen. Arrange them in three rows of four stickers.

6 Write numbers 0 to 9 on the dot stickers. On the final two stickers write 'CALL' and 'ANSWER' or 'ANS' for short.

7 Paint the felt-tip pen lids black and glue them to the top of the box.

You have set the scene and made some props. Now you can begin to play the part of a police officer in these role plays.

The missing ring

Play the part of a police officer at the front desk of a police station in this scene. Find out what happens when a boy brings a lost ring to the police station.

POLICE OFFICER: Good morning. How can I help you?

JOHNNY: I found this gold ring on the pavement.

POLICE OFFICER: Good boy. You did the right thing bringing it here.

JOHNNY: Maybe it's lost treasure?

POLICE OFFICER: No… just a very nice diamond ring, but it looks very valuable. Somebody must be missing it!

 JOHNNY: I hope we find them.

 POLICE OFFICER: We'll solve this case in no time. I'll look at my computer to see if anyone has reported it missing…

WHAT HAPPENS NEXT?

You can decide what happens next in this scene. Below are some fun ideas that you could try acting out using your own words. Then have a go at making up your own scenes.

1. A man dashes to the front desk. It's his wedding day and he's lost the ring. He gives Johnny a reward for handing it in.

2. The police officer telephones a woman who reported a lost ring. She says it can't be her ring because she lost a silver ring.

3. Johnny says he wishes he'd kept the ring. The police officer says that we should always hand in lost property to the police station.

Help, I'm lost!

Play the part of a police officer working outside in the community in this scene. Find out how she helps a boy who gets lost in the park.

 EDDIE: Help, I'm lost!

 POLICE OFFICER: Oh dear. What happened to you?

EDDIE: I got lost in the park…
(*Eddie starts to cry.*)

POLICE OFFICER: It's OK. I can help you. What's your name?

EDDIE: It's Eddie Brown. My mummy will be cross.

 POLICE OFFICER: Don't worry Eddie. We'll get you home to mum.

 EDDIE: Thank you.

 POLICE OFFICER: Eddie, do you know your mummy's telephone number or your address?

WHAT HAPPENS NEXT?

You can decide what happens next in this scene. Below are some fun ideas that you could try acting out using your own words. Then have a go at making up your own scenes.

1 Eddie says he knows his mother's **mobile number** and home telephone number. The police officer says he's very clever and calls his mother to collect him.

2 Eddie remembers his address. The police officer takes him home in a police car.

3 The police officer takes Eddie to the police station. His mummy is waiting there to take him home.

The bike accident

Play the part of a police officer helping at the scene of a road accident. Find out how he helps a boy who had fallen off his bike.

 PASSER BY: Help, a young boy has fallen off his bike in the road.

 JAKE: Oh no… my leg hurts.

 POLICE OFFICER: Let me help. Can you get up?

 JAKE: Yes… but it hurts. Is my bike OK?

(*Jake starts to cry.*)

POLICE OFFICER: Don't worry. Your bike isn't broken.

 JAKE: Oh good. It's a new bike, and my mum would go mad if I'd broken it.

 POLICE OFFICER: Now let's take a look at that leg of yours…

WHAT HAPPENS NEXT?

You can decide what happens next in this scene. Below are some fun ideas that you could try acting out using your own words. Then have a go at making up your own scenes.

1. The police officer says, 'I think your leg is broken'. He gets on his police radio and says, 'We need an ambulance'.

2. The police officer takes Jake home in the police car. He tells him to be more careful in future.

3. Jake says he's fine and wants to go home on his bike. The police officer watches Jake cycle away safely.

Caught in the act!

Have fun playing the parts of the police officers and burglars in this scene.

POLICE OFFICER 1 (*on the personal radio at the front desk*): Emergency! There's a burglary at the local jewellery shop.

POLICE OFFICER 2: Quick, get in the car.
(*Police officers pretend to get into a car and race to the crime scene.*)

POLICE OFFICER 1 (*speaks into personal radio*): We've arrived at the shop. The window is broken. The alarms are going off. We're going in...

BURGLAR 1: Look out, it's the police!

BURGLAR 2: Come on, let's go out the back.

POLICE OFFICER 1 (*police officer spots the burglars*): Look! They're getting away.

POLICE OFFICER 2: Oh no they're not.

BURGLARS: (starting to run): Oh yes we are.

POLICE OFFICERS: (police officers catch the burglars before they can escape): Oh no you're not. You're caught in the act!

(continued over page)

Caught in the act! (continued)

 BURGLAR 1: It wasn't us! We were just looking around.

 POLICE OFFICER 1: We know it was you.
But let's take your fingerprints as **evidence**!
(Police officers take the burglars' fingerprints.)

 POLICE OFFICER 2: If these match the prints on the broken window, you're in big trouble.

 BURGLAR 1 (*to burglar 2*): This was all your idea. I knew it wouldn't work…

WHAT HAPPENS NEXT?

You can decide what happens next in this scene. Below are some fun ideas that you could try acting out using your own words. Then have a go at making up your own scenes.

1 The fingerprints don't match the fingerprints at the shop. The police officers have to let the burglars go.

2 The fingerprints match the fingerprints found at the shop. The burglars are put in the police cell.

3 The police officers put the burglars in the police cell. Later that night the burglars escape from the cell.

GLOSSARY

advice A suggestion from someone about what you should do.

beat An area patrolled by a police officer on foot.

burglary Theft from a building or vehicle.

community All the people living in a particular area.

directions Instructions that tell you how to get somewhere.

evidence Facts or information which show something to be true.

fingerprints The marks made by the tips of your fingers when you touch something. Every person has a different set of fingerprints.

handcuffs A pair of metal clamps that lock a person's hands together to prevent them from escaping.

law The rules of a country which tell people what they can and cannot do.

mobile number The number you need to dial to contact someone on their mobile phone.

personal radio A device for sending and receiving voice signals over a long distance.

police neighbourhood support officer A member of the police force whose job is to make neighbourhoods safer.

solve To find an answer to a problem or puzzle.

suspect Someone who police think may have broken the law.

uniform A set of clothes worn by people at work or school.

INDEX

accidents 5, 18–19

burglars 5, 20-23

community 5, 16

crimes 8, 10

emergencies 5, 9, 12, 20

evidence 22

fingerprints 10, 11, 22, 23

front desk 8–9, 14, 15

handcuffs 6

law 5

police badge 6

police cell 23

radios 6, 12–13, 19, 20

role plays 14–23

station 8, 10–11, 12, 14, 15, 17

suspects 10, 11

uniform 6–7

Play the Part

Contents of books in the series:

Chef 978 07502 6509 6

What is a chef?
Things to make and do
What do chefs wear?
The chef's kitchen
Healthy food
Create your own café
Play the part
The best birthday cake ever!
The fruit salad saga
Sizzling sausages!
Pizza or pie?
Pizza or pie? (continued)

Firefighter 978 07502 6506 5

What do firefighters do?
Things to make and do
Dress like a firefighter
The fire engine
Putting out the fire
The fire station
Play the part
Emergency, car on fire!
Smoke alarm drama
Cat rescue
Run, it's the fire alarm!
Run, it's the fire alarm! (continued)

Shopkeeper 978 07502 6507 2

What do shopkeepers do?
Things to make and do
Different kinds of shops
Take a trip to the shops
Let's play shops!
Stocking and stacking
Play the part
The birthday present
Shiny shoes and football boots
My robot has broken down!
Come dine with me
Come dine with me (continued)

Doctor and Nurse 978 07502 6508 9

What do doctors and nurses do?
Things to make and do
Dress like a doctor or a nurse
A medical bag
The doctor's surgery
The children's ward
The x-ray machine
Play the part
A busy day
Oh no, broken bones!
Accident in the doctor's surgery
Accident in the doctor's surgery (continued)

Police Officer 978 07502 6504 1

What is a police officer?
Things to make and do
Dress like a police officer
The front desk
The police station
Offi cers on call!
Play the part
The missing ring
Help, I'm lost!
The bike accident
Caught in the act!
Caught in the act! (continued)

Train Driver 978 07502 6505 8

What is a train driver?
Things to make and do
Day in the life of a train driver
Dress like a train driver
The ticket inspector
In the driver's seat
All aboard!
Play the part
The Seaside Express
Tickets please!
Snow on the tracks
Snow on the tracks (continued)

WAYLAND